# 小帕帮大忙

【美】芭芭拉·德鲁波提斯◎著

【美】瑞贝卡·桑伯罗◎绘

范晓星◎译

天津出版传媒集团

新蕾出版社

**图书在版编目（CIP）数据**

小帕帮大忙/(美)德鲁波提斯(deRubertis,B.)
著;(美)桑伯罗(Thornburgh,R.)绘;范晓星译.--
天津:新蕾出版社,2016.3(2024.12重印)
（数学帮帮忙·互动版）
书名原文:Count on Pablo
ISBN 978-7-5307-6368-1

Ⅰ.①小⋯ Ⅱ.①德⋯②桑⋯③范⋯ Ⅲ.①数学–
儿童读物Ⅳ.①O1–49

中国版本图书馆 CIP 数据核字(2016)第 039279 号

**出版发行**：天津出版传媒集团
新蕾出版社
http://www.newbuds.com.cn
**地　　址**：天津市和平区西康路 35 号(300051)
**出 版 人**：马玉秀
**电　　话**：总编办 (022)23332422
发行部 (022)23332679　23332351
**传　　真**：(022)23332422
**经　　销**：全国新华书店
**印　　刷**：天津新华印务有限公司
**开　　本**：787mm×1092mm　1/16
**印　　张**：3
**版　　次**：2016 年 3 月第 1 版　2024 年 12 月第 21 次印刷
**定　　价**：12.00 元

著作权所有,请勿擅用本书制作各类出版物,违者必究。
如发现印、装质量问题,影响阅读,请与本社发行部联系调换。
地址:天津市和平区西康路 35 号
电话:(022)23332351　邮编:300051

# 无处不在的数学

资深编辑 卢 江

　　人们常说"兴趣是最好的老师",有了兴趣,学习就会变得轻松愉快。数学对于孩子来说或许有些难,因为比起语文,数学显得枯燥、抽象,不容易理解,孩子往往不那么喜欢。可许多家长都知道,学数学对于孩子的成长和今后的生活有多么重要。不仅数学知识很有用,学习数学过程中获得的数学思想和方法更会影响孩子的一生,因为数学素养是构成人基本素质的一个重要因素。但是,怎样才能让孩子对数学产生兴趣呢?怎样才能激发他们兴致勃勃地去探索数学问题呢?我认为,让孩子读些有趣的书或许是不错的选择。读了这套"数学帮帮忙",我立刻产生了想把它们推荐给教师和家长朋友们的愿望,因为这真是一套会让孩子爱上数学的好书!

　　这套有趣的图书从美国引进,原出版者是美国资深教育专家。每本书讲述一个孩子们生活中的故事,由故事中出现的问题自然地引入一个数学知识,然后通过运用数学知识解决问题。比如,从帮助外婆整理散落的纽扣引出分类,从为小狗记录藏骨头的地点引出空间方位等等。故事素材全部来源于孩子们的真实生活，不是童话，不是幻想，而是鲜活的生活实例。正是这些发生在孩子身边的故事，让孩子们懂得，数学无处不在并且非常有用；这些鲜活的实例也使得抽象的概念更易于理解，更容易激发孩子学习数学的兴趣，让他们逐渐爱上数学。这样的教育思想和方法与我国近年来提倡的数学教育理念是十分吻合的！

这是一套适合5~8岁孩子阅读的书，书中的有趣情节和生动的插画可以将抽象的数学问题直观化、形象化，为孩子的思维活动提供具体形象的支持。如果亲子共读的话，家长可以带领孩子推测情节的发展，探讨解决难题的办法，让孩子在愉悦的氛围中学到知识和方法。

值得教师和家长朋友们注意的是，在每本书的后面，出版者还加入了"互动课堂"及"互动练习"，一方面通过一些精心设计的活动让孩子巩固新学到的数学知识，进一步体会知识的含义和实际应用；另一方面帮助家长指导孩子阅读，体会故事中数学之外的道理，逐步提升孩子的阅读理解能力。

我相信孩子读过这套书后一定会明白，原来，数学不是烦恼，不是包袱，数学真能帮大忙！

赶集的日子到了！小帕第一次到奶奶的小摊上帮忙。他都等不及了。

　　"是不是该走了？"小帕问奶奶。

　　"再等等。"奶奶回答，"我们要摘好菜才能出发啊。"

3

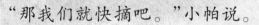

“那我们就快摘吧。”小帕说。

“好,小帕。”奶奶笑着说,“你去摘青柠檬吧。”

小帕蹦蹦跳跳地来到青柠檬树下,“我要摘几个呢?”

“大概二十个吧。”奶奶说,“挑大的摘!”

小帕一边从树上摘下青柠檬，一边大声地数：

**1, 2, 3, 4, 5,**
**6, 7, 8, 9, 10,**
**11, 12, 13, 14, 15,**
**16, 17, 18, 19, 20。**

"数得真棒！"奶奶夸奖他。

　　"现在我们可以走了吧？"
小帕问。

　　"只卖青柠檬吗？"奶奶说。
她指了指旁边的筐，"我们还
要把这些洋葱洗干净，一对一
对地拴在一起，就像这样。"

　　说着，奶奶把两个洋葱的
叶子系在一起。

　　小帕飞快地洗洋葱，然后把它们两个两个地
系起来。他的衣服都湿了，可他一点儿都不在乎。

"你把洋葱数一数好吗？"奶奶问。

"我要两个两个地数,这样数得快。"小帕说,"奶奶,您听我数。"

奶奶用心地听,小帕开始数了:

**2,4,6,8,10,**
**12,14,16,18,20,**
**22,24,26,28,30,**
**32,34,36,38,40。**

"数得真棒!"奶奶夸奖他。

"现在我们可以走了吧？"小帕问。

"还不行。"奶奶说，"我需要你帮我把这些辣椒洗一洗，然后把它们五个五个地装在塑料袋里，再告诉我咱们一共有多少辣椒。"

"我动作可快呢，奶奶！"小帕说。他飞快地洗好辣椒，身上的衣服更湿了，可他一点儿都不在乎。

"我要五个五个地数辣椒。"小帕说,"这样数更快。"

5,10,15,20,25,

30,35,40,45,50,

55,60,65,70,75,

80,85,90,95,100。

"数得真棒!"奶奶夸奖他。

　　"现在我们都准备好了吗？"小帕刚问完，发现奶奶又搬来五筐西红柿。"哦，不！"小帕沮丧地说，"我们永远都去不了市场了！"

　　"这是我们最后一项任务了。"奶奶说，"我们只要把西红柿洗干净，十个十个地放进盒子里就好了。"

　　不一会儿，小帕就把西红柿洗得干干净净，红里透亮。不过，他自己已经变成了一个小泥猴！

"我要十个十个地数西红柿。这么数特别快！奶奶，您听着啊。"小帕说。

10，20，30，40，50，

60，70，80，90，100，

110，120，130，140，150，

160，170，180，190，200。

"数得真棒！"奶奶说。

"我差点儿把香菜忘了。"奶奶说完,在每个装西红柿的盒子里塞了一小把香菜。"漂亮吗,小帕?"

"很漂亮。"小帕说,"我们现在可以去市场了吧?"

奶奶摇了摇头，"还有件'东西'要好好洗一洗！"

小帕一下就猜到了，奶奶是在说他呢！"我马上就来！"他说。不一会儿，他就洗得干干净净，和奶奶出发去市场了。

"终于出发啦！"小帕说。

市场里熙熙攘攘，人声鼎沸。小帕四处张望，发现好多摊位在卖非常有趣的东西。市场上甚至还有一个乐队在演奏音乐。

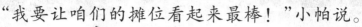

"今天这儿的摊位可真不少。"奶奶说。

"我要让咱们的摊位看起来最棒！"小帕说。

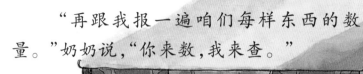

"再跟我报一遍咱们每样东西的数量。"奶奶说,"你来数,我来查。"

老奶奶蔬果摊

于是,小帕把摊位搭好,十个十个、五个五个、两个两个、一个一个地数起来。

"你真是个好帮手，数数也特别棒。"奶奶说。

奶奶和小帕等顾客来买东西。市场上人来人往，可没人在奶奶的摊位前驻足，一位顾客都没有。

　　小帕开始担心了：要是奶奶一样东西都卖不出去怎么办？

　　几个小时过去了。他们还是没有卖出一样东西。

　　小帕肚子饿了。"我可以到加西亚先生那儿买一袋玉米片吗？"他问。

　　"可以。"奶奶说，"我也有点儿饿了。"

小帕买了一大袋玉米片。他一边嚼一边往回走，心想：要是我有一些……突然他有了一个好主意。"奶奶！"他喊起来。

"出什么事啦？"奶奶问。

"我们可以做莎莎酱来配玉米片！"小帕说，"我们需要的材料全都有！一个青柠檬、两个洋葱、五个辣椒、十个西红柿……"

"还有一小把香菜！"奶奶说。

　　"做莎莎酱,这个主意太棒了!"奶奶说,"你去马
丁内斯阿姨那儿买一个漂亮的碗来。我去找加西亚
先生借两把刀和一个勺。"

小帕一回来，马上就开始叮叮当当地切菜，西红柿、辣椒和洋葱四处飞溅。

"小帕，慢一点儿！"奶奶说，"你切得太快了！"

奶奶把青柠檬汁挤到大碗里，小帕把五颜六色的蔬菜搅拌均匀。

"来尝尝吧。"小帕说。

奶奶用玉米片舀起一点儿莎莎酱,放进嘴里。"好吃!"她说。

小帕也尝了一口。真的很好吃!"现在,我们去听听别人尝过这莎莎酱会怎么说吧。"他满心期待地说。

小帕站在一大碗
漂亮的莎莎酱和一大袋玉米片旁
边。"尝一尝，看一看！美味的莎莎
酱配玉米片！"他大声吆喝。

很快人们就聚拢在周围。他们
尝过莎莎酱以后都说："味道
好极了！你们是怎么做的？"

小帕告诉大家："你们需要十个西红柿、
五个辣椒、两个洋葱、一个青柠檬……"

"和一小把香菜。"奶奶说。

"我正想要做这道菜！"一位大伯说。

"我也是！"大家七嘴八舌。

小帕和奶奶忙得四脚朝天。没一会儿，他们的摊位
前就安静了。原来，奶奶带来的蔬果全都卖光了！

　　"奶奶，"小帕说，"我们把带来的蔬果都卖光了。20 个青柠檬、40 个洋葱、100 个辣椒和200 个西红柿！"

　　"还有 20 把香菜呢！我可从来没这么忙过！"奶奶说。

现在，一到赶集的日子，顾客们就聚在奶奶的摊位前。大家是来买小帕莎莎酱原材料的。那可是最好吃的莎莎酱！

31

# 数 字 表

| 1 | 2 | 3 | 4 | 5 | 6 | 7 | 8 | 9 | 10 |
|---|---|---|---|---|---|---|---|---|---|
| 11 | 12 | 13 | 14 | 15 | 16 | 17 | 18 | 19 | 20 |
| 21 | 22 | 23 | 24 | 25 | 26 | 27 | 28 | 29 | 30 |
| 31 | 32 | 33 | 34 | 35 | 36 | 37 | 38 | 39 | 40 |
| 41 | 42 | 43 | 44 | 45 | 46 | 47 | 48 | 49 | 50 |
| 51 | 52 | 53 | 54 | 55 | 56 | 57 | 58 | 59 | 60 |
| 61 | 62 | 63 | 64 | 65 | 66 | 67 | 68 | 69 | 70 |
| 71 | 72 | 73 | 74 | 75 | 76 | 77 | 78 | 79 | 80 |
| 81 | 82 | 83 | 84 | 85 | 86 | 87 | 88 | 89 | 90 |
| 91 | 92 | 93 | 94 | 95 | 96 | 97 | 98 | 99 | 100 |

亲爱的家长朋友，请您和孩子一起完成下面这些内容，会有更大的收获哟！

## 提高阅读能力

• 阅读封面，包括书名、作者等内容，然后和孩子聊聊小帕帮奶奶卖蔬果如何热心而且有责任感，值得奶奶信任。

• 读过故事后，请孩子回答下面的问题：你觉得小帕以前跟奶奶去过市场吗？为什么？小帕为什么想让奶奶的摊位最显眼最漂亮？奶奶可以信赖小帕吗？你怎么知道的？

• 一边表演一边复述故事。家长可以准备一些物品，比如纽扣等，然后鼓励孩子扮演小帕，一个一个、两个两个、五个五个、十个十个地数。

## 巩固数学概念

• 请孩子数故事里出现的东西，比如小帕去市场前洗过的东西。（别忘了数小帕哟！）

• 小帕数不同的蔬果用了不同的数法。小帕数青柠檬的时候，可以两个两个、五个五个、十个十个地数吗？你会用什么方法数青柠檬？

为什么？

• 请看第 32 页的数字表。

两个两个地数，每隔一个数字画"/"。

五个五个地数，每第五个数字后画"\"。

十个十个地数，每第十个数字后画"－"。

让孩子试着用上面不同的方法数数吧！

## 生活中的数学

• 请用第 31 页的食谱来制作莎莎酱。（切完辣椒和洋葱后别忘了洗手哟！）

• 请孩子想想，如果想做两倍、三倍或者一半的莎莎酱需要多少材料。

一个一个地数出西红柿和洋葱各有多少个，比一比用哪种形式摆放好数一些？

请你试着两个两个地数这些苹果，在□中写出每次数得的数。

五个五个地数这些猕猴桃,共有多少个? 想一想,要数多少次?

37

两个两个地数这些草莓，一共要数多少次？找一找，哪些草莓五个五个地数和两个两个地数时都要数到？

这些西瓜一共有多少个? 你想怎样数?

方格中少了一些数，你能写出来吗？

方格中缺少的这些数，哪些是五个五个地数需要的数，哪些是两个两个地数需要的数？

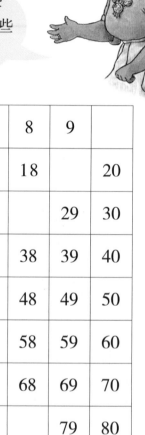

|    | 2  | 3  | 4  | 5  | 6  | 7  | 8  | 9  |    |
|----|----|----|----|----|----|----|----|----|----|
| 11 |    | 13 | 14 | 15 | 16 | 17 | 18 |    | 20 |
| 21 | 22 |    | 24 | 25 | 26 | 27 |    | 29 | 30 |
| 31 | 32 | 33 |    | 35 | 36 |    | 38 | 39 | 40 |
| 41 | 42 | 43 | 44 |    |    | 47 | 48 | 49 | 50 |
| 51 | 52 | 53 | 54 |    |    | 57 | 58 | 59 | 60 |
| 61 | 62 | 63 |    | 65 | 66 |    | 68 | 69 | 70 |
| 71 | 72 |    | 74 | 75 | 76 | 77 |    | 79 | 80 |
| 81 |    | 83 | 84 | 85 | 86 | 87 | 88 |    | 90 |
|    | 92 | 93 | 94 | 95 | 96 | 97 | 98 | 99 |    |

请你试着把 1 个柠檬、2 个洋葱和 4 个辣椒分成一份，看看上面这些能分成几份，有剩余的吗？

41

**互动练习 1：**

西红柿和洋葱各 20 个。洋葱的摆放形式好数一些。

**互动练习 2：**

| 2 | 4 | 6 | 8 | 10 | 12 | 14 | 16 | 18 | 20 | 22 | 24 | 26 | 28 | 30 |
| 32 | 34 | 36 | 38 | 40 |

**互动练习 3：**

猕猴桃共有 50 个，一共要数 10 次。

**互动练习 4：**

一共要数 25 次。其中 10、20、30、40、50 这些数对应的草莓在五个五个地数和两个两个地数时都要数到。

**互动练习 5：**

一共有 12 个西瓜。数法不唯一，略。

**互动练习 6：**

缺少的数：1、10、12、19、23、28、34、37、45、46、55、56、64、67、73、78、82、89、91、100。

五个五个地数需要的数：10、45、55、100。

两个两个地数需要的数：10、12、28、34、46、56、64、78、82、100。

**互动练习 7：**

能分成 10 份，最后剩余 8 个辣椒。

（习题设计：何　晨）

# Count on Pablo

It was market day! For the first time, Pablo was going to help his *abuela* (his grandmother) with her market stand. He could hardly wait.

"Is it time to go? " Pablo called.

"Not yet," said Abuela. "We can't go until we pick some things to sell! "

"Let's pick FAST," said Pablo.

"Okay, Pablo! " Abuela laughed. "You can pick the limes."

Pablo scurried up the lime tree. "How many should I pick? "

"About twenty," said Abuela. "Nice big ones! "

As Pablo twisted the limes off the tree, he counted them in a loud voice.

$$1, 2, 3, 4, 5,$$
$$6, 7, 8, 9, 10,$$
$$11, 12, 13, 14, 15,$$
$$16, 17, 18, 19, 20.$$

"Good counting! " Abuela called.

"Now can we go? " Pablo asked.

"With only limes to sell? " said Abuela. She pointed to a bucket. "First we have to wash these onions and tie them in pairs, like this."

Abuela made a knot with the tops of two onions.

Pablo washed and tied the onions quickly. He got all wet, but he didn't mind.

"Could you count the onions? " Abuela asked.

"I'll count them by twos. That's a fast way to count," said Pablo. "Listen, Abuela."

Abuela listened. Pablo counted.

2, 4, 6, 8, 10,
12, 14, 16, 18, 20,
22, 24, 26, 28, 30,
32, 34, 36, 38, 40.

"Good counting! " said Abuela.

"Now can we go? " asked Pablo.

"Not yet," said Abuela. "I need you to wash these peppers. Put five in each plastic bag. Then tell me how many peppers we have."

"I'll hurry, Abuela! " said Pablo. He washed the peppers very quickly and got even wetter. But that was okay with Pablo.

"I'll count the peppers by fives," said Pablo. "That's a faster way to count."

5, 10, 15, 20, 25,
30, 35, 40, 45, 50,
55, 60, 65, 70, 75,
80, 85, 90, 95, 100.

"Good counting! " Abuela called.

"Now are we ready? " Pablo asked . Then he saw that Abuela had five buckets of tomatoes."Oh, no! " cried Pablo."We'll NEVER get to the market! "

"It's our last job," said Abuela. "We just have to wash the tomatoes and put ten in each box."

Before long Pablo had the tomatoes clean and shiny. But he was a muddy mess!

"I'll count the tomatoes by tens. That's a VERY fast way to count! Listen, Abuela," said Pablo.

10, 20, 30, 40, 50,
60, 70, 80, 90, 100,
110, 120, 130, 140, 150,
160, 170, 180, 190, 200.

"Good counting! " said Abuela.

"I almost forgot the cilantro," Abuela said. She tucked a little bunch of the herbs into each box of tomatoes. "Isn't that pretty, Pablo? "

"Very pretty," said Pablo. "But can we PLEASE go to the market now? "

Abuela shook her head. "One more thing needs to be washed! "

Pablo knew she meant HIM. "I'll really hurry!" he said. In no time he was all cleaned up, and they were on their way.

"Finally! " said Pablo.

The market was crowded and noisy. Everywhere Pablo looked, he saw people selling the most wonderful things. There was even a band playing music.

"There are so many stands here today," Abuela said.

"I'll make our stand look the best! " said Pablo.

"Tell me again how many we have of everything," said Abuela. "You count and I'll check."

So, after Pablo set up the stand, he counted by tens, by fives, by twos, and by ones.

"You are a good helper and a very good counter," said Abuela.

Abuela and Pablo waited for shoppers to come. Many people were at the market. But nobody stopped at Abuela's stand. Nobody at all.

Pablo began to worry. What if Abuela didn't sell anything?

Hours went by. Still they had not sold a thing.

Pablo was getting hungry. "May I buy a bag of tortilla chips from Señor Garcia? " he asked.

"Yes," said Abuela. "I'm a little hungry, too."

Pablo bought a big bag of chips. As he walked back munching, he thought, "I wish I had some..." Suddenly he had a great idea. "Abuela! " he shouted.

"What is it? " asked Abuela.

"We could make salsa to go with these chips! " said Pablo. "Everything we need is right here! 1 lime, 2 onions, 5 peppers, 10 tomatoes..."

"...and a little bunch of cilantro! " said Abuela.

"Making salsa is a wonderful idea! " Abuela said. "Go buy a pretty bowl from Señora Martinez. I'll borrow two knives and a spoon from Señor Garcia."

The minute Pablo returned, he began to chop, chop, chop. Bits of tomato and pepper and onion flew everywhere.

"Slow down, Pablo!" said Abuela. "You are chopping too fast!"

Abuela squeezed the lime juice into the bowl. Then Pablo mixed the bright colors together.

"Let's taste it," said Pablo.

Abuela scooped up some salsa with a tortilla chip and popped it in her mouth. "Delicious!" she said.

Pablo tasted the salsa, too. It was delicious. "Now we'll see what happens when other people taste our salsa," he said.

Pablo stood right next to the beautiful bowl of salsa and the big bag of chips. "Taste our delicious salsa!" he called.

Soon people were crowding around. They tasted the salsa. "Delicious!" they said. "How do you make this salsa?"

Pablo told them. "You need 10 tomatoes, 5 peppers, 2 onions, 1 lime ..."

"...and a little bunch of cilantro," said Abuela.

"Then that's what I want!" said a man. "I do, too!" said a dozen voices.

It was very busy. Then it was very quiet. Abeula's stand was empty!

"Abuela," said Pablo, "we sold everything! 20 limes! 40 onions! 100 peppers! 200 tomatoes!"

"And 20 little bunches of cilantro! I've never had such a busy day!" said Abuela.

Now on market day, shoppers hurry to Abuela's stand. There they buy everything they need to make Pablo's Salsa. Delicious!